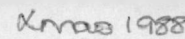

Xmas 1988

To Shaz

BRILL
ADVICE!

Love Trace xx

"... well, what
else do you give
the girl who's got
everything?!"

Here's to the girlies in '89
— let's see what messes
we can get into this time!
Love, hugs
+ brilliant advice,
Weezter
Z

BRILLIANT ADVICE!

BY ANNIE LAWSON

A Deirdre McDonald Book
BELLEW PUBLISHING
London

First published in 1988
by Deirdre McDonald Books
Bellew Publishing Co. Ltd.
7 Southampton Place, London WC1A 2DR

ISBN 0 947792 13 9

Printed in Great Britain by
Richard Clay (The Chaucer Press) Ltd,
Bungay, Suffolk

charged with
EMOTIONAL INADEQUACY
I've never had A RELATIONSHIP with you! I've just had 465 one-night-stands with the same person!

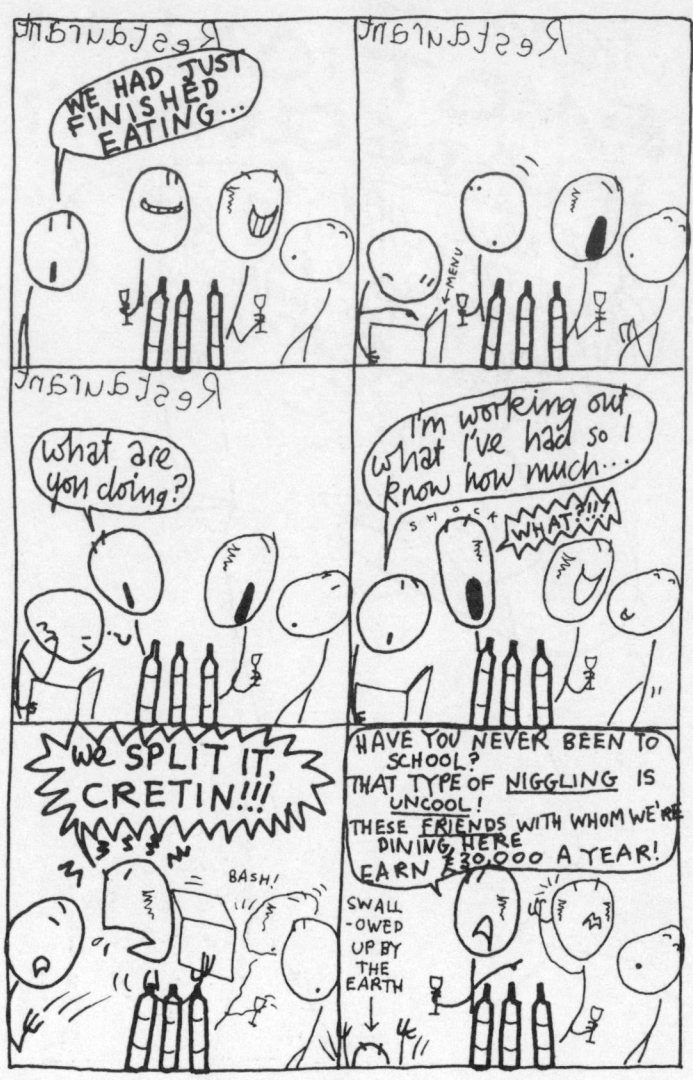

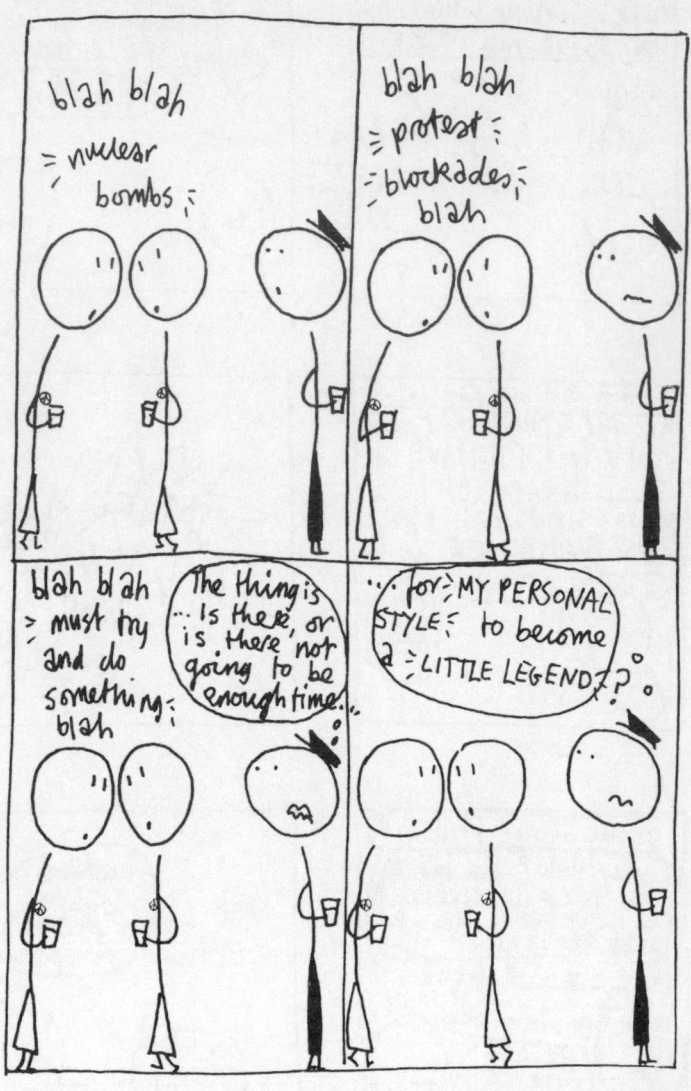

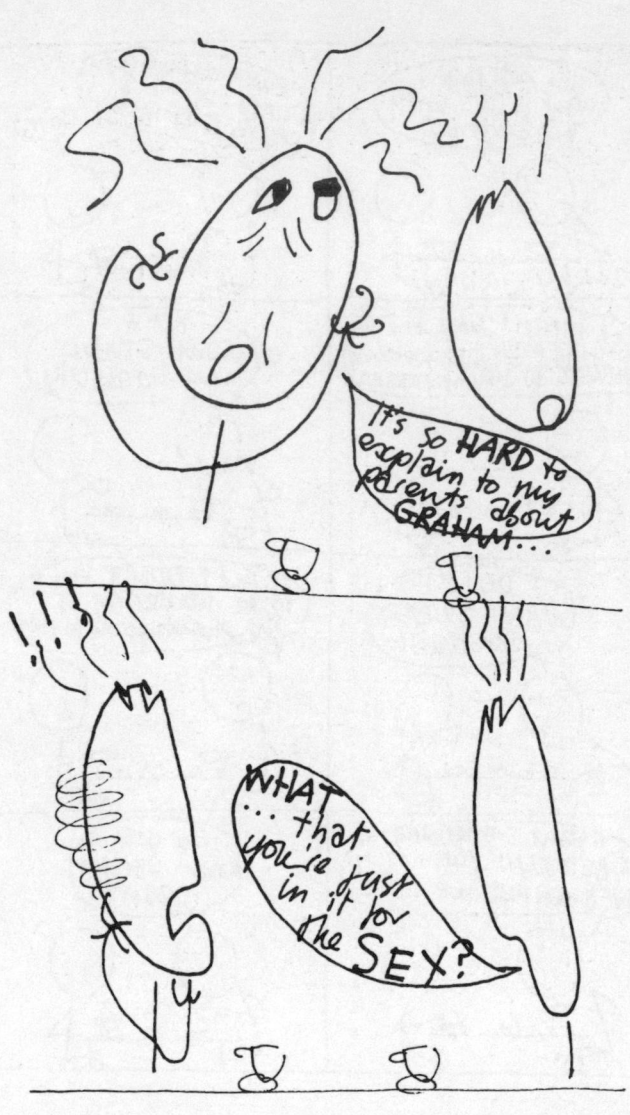

PRE-MENSTRUAL -TENSION

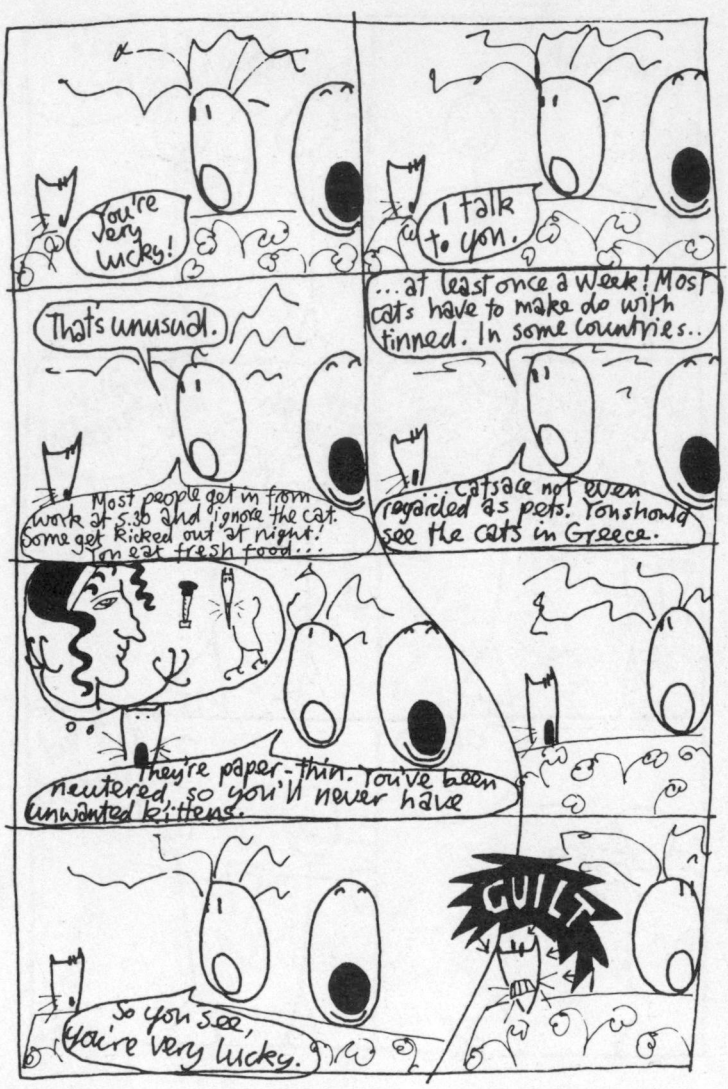